REVISE KEY STAGE 2 SATs
Mathematics

TARGETED PRACTICE NUMBER, RATIO AND ALGEBRA

Series Consultant: Janice Pimm

Authors: Christopher Bishop and Brian Speed

Also available:

Revise Mathematics Key Stage 2 SATs Targeted Practice
Arithmetic 9781292146218

Revise Mathematics Key Stage 2 SATs Targeted Practice
Geometry, Measures and Statistics 9781292146225

Contents

A small bit of small print

The Standards and Testing Agency publishes Sample Test Materials on its website. This is the official content and this book should be used in conjunction with it. The questions in this book have been written to help you practise what you have learned in your revision. Remember: the real test questions may not look like this.

Introduction

About your tests

At the end of Year 6, you will take tests to find out about your maths skills. This book will help you revise your **number**, **ratio and algebra** skills.

- There will be one **arithmetic** test. This test will ask you to carry out calculations. You will have 30 minutes to do this test.

- There will be two **reasoning** tests. These tests will ask you to solve problems. You will have 40 minutes to do each test.

Using this book

Each page of this book is about a different maths skill. Use the checkboxes at the top of the page to track your progress:

Had a go ☐   Tick this box when you've read the page.

Nearly there ☐   Tick this box when you understand the page quite well.

Nailed it! ☐   Tick this box when you understand the page really well.

Place value

1. Write twelve thousand, one hundred and eighty-four in figures.

.... **1 mark**

2. Write 324,672 in words.

.... **1 mark**

3. Write these numbers in order of size from smallest to largest.

456   299   901   472   575

.... **1 mark**

4. Here are three digit cards. Use one card to make each of these statements correct.

    [5]   [6]   [7]

a)

[5][6] > [ ][0]

b)

[7][6] < [ ][7]

1 mark   **1 mark**

5. Write the letter which points to the number 50,000

    A B   C   D   E
    ↓ ↓   ↓   ↓   ↓
    ├─┼──┼──┼──┼──┼──┼──┼──┼──┼──┼─→
    0   1 million

.... **1 mark**

6. Use the digits 2, 3 and 4 once each to make the multiplication with the greatest possible product. Write your answer.

> You can make a two-digit number and a one-digit number with the three digits.

....   ✕   ....   = ...   **2 marks**

Negative numbers

1. These thermometers show the temperatures in Sheffield and Barcelona on a winter's night.

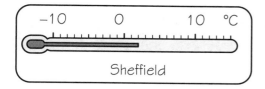
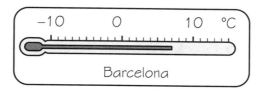

     Sheffield   Barcelona

     a) How many degrees colder is it in Sheffield than it is in Barcelona?

                                                ....   **1 mark**

     b) On another night, the temperature in Barcelona is 4 °C. In Sheffield it is 7 degrees cooler. What is the temperature in Sheffield?

                                                ....   **1 mark**

2. Circle the two numbers that have a difference of 2

> The difference is the size of the gap between the two numbers.

    −1   −0.5   0   0.5   1

                                                    1 mark

3. Here is a table of temperatures at dawn on the same day.

temperature (°C)	
London	−4
Moscow	−6
New York	−9
Paris	+6
Sydney	+14

     a) What is the difference in temperature between London and Paris?

                                                ....   **1 mark**

     b) At noon the temperature in New York has risen by 5 °C. What is the temperature in New York at noon?

                                                ....   **1 mark**

Decimal numbers

1. Tick each of the cards that show more than a half.

| 0.75 | 0.7 | 0.37 | 0.34 | 0.8 | 0.66 | 0.35 |

1 mark

2. In this grid, the three numbers in each row and column add up to 15
   Fill in the empty square.

2.5	4.6	7.9
7.1		1.2
5.4	3.7	5.9

1 mark

3. Write these numbers in order of size, starting with the smallest.

   1.01   1.001   1.101   0.11

   .... **1 mark**

4. Write three decimals greater than zero that
   add together to make 0.1

   > Think of decimal numbers with two or more decimal places.

   .... **1 mark**

3

Rounding

1. For each set of numbers, draw lines from the numbers in the top row to the nearest hundred in the bottom row.

   a)

   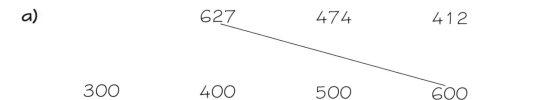

   | 627 | 474 | 412 |

   | 300 | 400 | 500 | 600 | 700 |

   1 mark

   b)

   | 531 | 617 | 253 | 474 |

   | 200 | 300 | 400 | 500 | 600 | 700 |

   2 marks

2. Round the following numbers.

   a) 540 to the nearest 100   ....   1 mark

   b) 236 to the nearest 10   ....   1 mark

   c) 2650 to the nearest 1,000   ....   1 mark

3. Draw lines from the numbers in the top row to the nearest thousand in the bottom row.

   | 1,070 | 8,225 | 3,680 |

   | 4,000 | 9,000 | 3,000 | 1,000 | 8,000 |

   1 mark

4

Rounding decimals

1. Round these numbers to 1 decimal place.

   a) 8.21   .... 1 mark

   b) 0.35   .... 1 mark

   c) 100.24   .... 1 mark

   d) 0.019   .... 1 mark

> To round to 1 decimal place, look at the hundredths. To round to 2 decimal places, look at the thousandths.

2. Round these numbers to 2 decimal places.

   a) 1.245   .... 1 mark

   b) 23.521   .... 1 mark

   c) 43.334   .... 1 mark

   d) 0.121212   .... 1 mark

3. Kavya runs a race. The time on the stop watch when she crosses the finish line is 16.25 seconds. Round this time to the nearest whole second.

   .... 1 mark

4. Kinjiro buys a box of cakes to share with his friends. He works out that the cost of each cake is 37.5 pence. What is the cost of each cake rounded to the nearest whole penny?

   .... 1 mark

Roman numerals

1. Write these Roman numerals in figures.

    a) VIII   ....8..............   **1 mark**

    b) XCV   ....   **1 mark**

    c) XXXIX   ....   **1 mark**

    d) DXL   ....   **1 mark**

> Remember these Roman numerals:
> | | |
> |---|---|
> | I = 1 | V = 5 |
> | X = 10 | L = 50 |
> | C = 100 | D = 500 |
> | M = 1000 | |

2. Solve this calculation written in Roman numerals. Write your answer in figures.

     D   +   C   −   L   =   ?

     ....   + ...   −   ....   = ...   **2 marks**

3. There is a sign above the entrance to Mulberry Drive Primary School that says MCMXCII. What year does this represent?

                                       ....   **1 mark**

4. Write the date in Roman numerals.

    a) 16 May 2004

    day of the month: ......XVI......

    month: ......V......

    year: ...MMIV...

> May is the 5th month, so it is represented by a V.

    b) 23 Jan 1993

    day of the month: ....

    month: ....

    year: ....   **3 marks**

Written addition

1. Complete these calculations.

> Line up the digits carefully.

a) 681 + 292

```
  6 8 1
+ 2 9 2
-------
  9 7 3
    1
```

.........973..........   **1 mark**

b) 436 + 382

....   **1 mark**

c) 1.25 + 0.82

....   **1 mark**

d) 5,235 + 5,263

....   **1 mark**

2. Fill in the three missing digits that make this addition correct.

```
      1   3  ☐
  +   3  ☐   7
  ----------
    ☐   1   8
        1
```

> Look at the boxes one at a time, starting with the ones column.

2 marks

3. This table shows the number of books borrowed from a library each day for three days.

   What was the total number of books borrowed on the three days?

day	Mon	Tue	Wed
number of books borrowed	3,426	2,312	1,091

....   **2 marks**

Written subtraction

1. Complete these calculations.

   a) 781 − 221

   ```
     7 8 1
   − 2 2 1
     5 6 0
   ```

   ....560...........　1 mark

   b) 4.9 − 2.5

   ....　1 mark

   c) 452 − 235

   ....　1 mark

   d) 12,984 − 1,287

   ....　1 mark

2. Two numbers add together to equal 1,000. One of the numbers is 573. What is the other number?

   > To find the answer, subtract 573 from 1,000

   ....　2 marks

3. The radius of the Earth is 6,371 kilometres. The radius of the planet Mars is 3,390 kilometres. What is the difference between the radius of Earth and the radius of Mars?

   ....　2 marks

4. Write the three missing digits to make this subtraction correct.

   > Work out the missing digits one at a time, starting with the ones column.

   ```
       ³4̶ ¹5 ☐
   −   2 ☐ 4
   ─────────
       ☐ 8 2
   ```

   2 marks

Estimating

1. Alfie buys a packet of biscuits. Tick the amount that the packet of biscuits is most likely to weigh.

   10 kg ☐   250 kg ☐

   1 g ☐   250 g ☐   **1 mark**

2. Here is a number line. In the box, estimate the number shown by the arrow.

   0 _____ 100

   > Estimating is finding a number that is close enough to the right answer. You do not need to work out the exact answer.

   1 mark

3. Estimate the answer to the following calculation:

   4,735 + 2,102 + 7,976 + 3,793 =

   > Round each number to the nearest 1,000

   ....   **1 mark**

4. A band plays three concerts. The numbers of fans at each concert are 15,457, 17,863 and 12,031. Approximately how many fans attended the three concerts in total?

   ....   **1 mark**

Multiples

1. Look at this list of numbers.

   3   63   18   42   311   422   16   9

   a) Circle the even numbers.   **1 mark**

   b) Tick the numbers that are multiples of 3   **1 mark**

2. Here is a number chart.

71	72	73	74	75	76	77	78	79	80
81	82	83	84	85	86	87	88	89	90
91	92	93	94	95	96	97	98	99	100

   a) Circle the smallest number on the chart that
      is a common multiple of 2 and 7

   > A common multiple is
   > a multiple of two or
   > more numbers.

                                                                                      1 mark

   b) Circle the largest number that is not a multiple of 2, 3 or 5   **1 mark**

3. Here is a diagram that can be used to sort numbers. Write one number
   from this list in each box:

               640   102   80   22

	less than 100	100 or more
multiple of 20		
not a multiple of 20		

                                                                                      4 marks

10

Factors

1. Write all the numbers between 50 and 100 that are factors of 180

   > Factors are numbers that divide exactly into another number.

   ....   1 mark

2. Write all the factors of 30 that are also factors of 20

   ....   1 mark

3. Write these numbers in the correct places on the diagram:

   > Write common factors in the middle section. Write numbers that don't belong in any section outside the diagram.

   5   6   7   8

   factors of 30   factors of 40

   4 marks

4. Theo and Andrew have 81 cans of cola in their shop. They want to arrange them in rows. What possible arrangements could they use?

   ....

   ....   2 marks

Prime numbers

1. Circle the two prime numbers in this list.

   29   39   49   59   69

   > A prime number only has two factors – itself and 1

   1 mark

2. Brian and Kathy play a number game. Kathy thinks of a number. Brian asks some questions and Kathy answers them. Here are the questions and answers:

   Is it under 20?   No.   Is it under 25?   Yes.

   Is it odd?   Yes.   Is it a prime number?   Yes.

   What was Kathy's number?   ....   1 mark

3. Akiko thinks that 77 is a prime number. Is she right? Explain how you know.

   ....

   ....   2 marks

4. Here is a diagram for sorting numbers. Write the numbers 9, 17 and 20 in the correct boxes.

   > One box will stay empty.

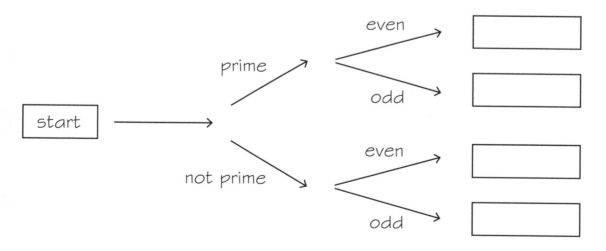

   3 marks

Square numbers

1. Work out these square numbers.

   a) 4^2 $4 \times 4 = 16$ ....16.................   1 mark

   b) 10^2 ....   1 mark

   c) 5^2 ....   1 mark

   d) 50^2 ....   1 mark

2. Here is a diagram that you can use to sort numbers. Sort these numbers into the diagram:

   16   25   11   1   14   8

	even	not even
square numbers	16	
not square numbers		

   2 marks

3. Find two square numbers that add up to 45

   .... + ... = 45   2 marks

4. Prakash has 25 stickers. He arranges them in rows to make a square. How many stickers are in each row?

   ....   1 mark

Cube numbers

1. Work out these cube numbers.

   a) 6^3 $6 \times 6 \times 6 = 216$ ....216........... 1 mark

   b) 1^3 .... 1 mark

   c) 4^3 .... 1 mark

   d) 10^3 .... 1 mark

2. Match each number with its cube number. One has been done for you.

| 7 | 5 | 3 | 10 | 1 |

| 1 | 1,000 | 125 | 343 | 27 | 4 marks |

3. Rebecca says, '64 is a square number.' Clint says, '64 is a cube number.'

   Explain why both Rebecca and Clint are correct. Use calculations to prove it.

   ....
   .... 2 marks

4. Work out how many small cubes are needed to make this cube.

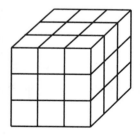

   You don't need to do any counting. The number of cubes is a cube number.

          .... 1 mark

Short multiplication

1. Complete these multiplications.

   a) 24 × 6

   b) 22 × 3

Leave a space under the answer line to carry digits.

```
      2 4
  ×     6
  ─────────
    1 4 4
      2
```

...........144............   1 mark

....   1 mark

   c) 253 × 4

   d) 472 × 5

....   1 mark

....   1 mark

2. Lewis is wrapping presents. He has seven presents to wrap. For each present, he needs 75 cm of wrapping paper. Use short multiplication to find out the total length of wrapping paper he needs.

....   1 mark

3. Niamh is taking part in a reading competition. She decides to read three books every week for a year. Use short multiplication to find out how many books she will read in a year.

There are 52 weeks in a year.

....   1 mark

Long multiplication

1. Complete these multiplications.

a) 24 × 16

```
        2 4
    ×   1 6
    ─────────
      2 4 0
      1 4²4
    ─────────
      3 8 4
```

........384........   2 marks

b) 22 × 16

....   2 marks

c) 31 × 22

....   2 marks

d) 46 × 28

....   2 marks

2. A musician sells CDs of her music for £13. In one month she sells 34 CDs.

   Use long multiplication to find out how much money she makes from selling CDs in that month.

....   2 marks

3. Hayden goes swimming once a week. Every time he goes swimming, he swims 18 lengths. How many lengths does he swim in 32 weeks?

....   2 marks

16

Short division

1. Complete these divisions.

   a) 98 ÷ 7

   $$\begin{array}{r} 1\ 4 \\ 7\overline{)9\,^2 8} \end{array}$$

   ....14.......... 1 mark

   b) 144 ÷ 6

   .... 1 mark

   c) 847 ÷ 7

   .... 1 mark

   d) 189 ÷ 9

   .... 1 mark

2. Write the missing number.

   30 ÷ .... = 6

   1 mark

3. Circle each number that has a remainder of 2 when divided by 5

   15   27   26   45   32   24

   2 marks

4. This bottle contains cough mixture.
   A spoonful of cough mixture is 5 ml.

   How many spoonfuls can you get from this bottle?

Cough mixture
375 ml

   .... 1 mark

Long division

1. Complete these divisions.

a) $432 \div 15$

```
        2 8 r 12
  1 5 ⌐4 3 2
      3 0 0  (15 × 20)
      ̅ ̅ ̅ ̅ ̅ ̅
      1 3 2
      1 2 0  (15 × 8)
      ̅ ̅ ̅ ̅ ̅ ̅
        1 2
```

.....28 r 12.....   1 mark

b) $924 \div 22$

....   1 mark

c) $626 \div 18$

....   1 mark

d) $811 \div 24$

....   1 mark

2. There are 234 pencils in a box. Joy shares them equally between 13 friends. How many pencils does each friend receive?

....   2 marks

Order of operations

1. Complete the calculations.

a) $6 \div 2 + 12$

$6 \div 2 = 3$

$3 + 12 = 15$

> Do any calculations in brackets first. Then do any multiplication and division. Do addition and subtraction last.

b) $6 \times 3 - 8$

...........15........... **1 mark**

.... **1 mark**

c) $(4 + 5) \times 8 - 1$

d) $(3 \times 4) \div (1 + 5)$

.... **1 mark**

.... **1 mark**

e) $(5 \times 3) + 12 - 6$

f) $12 - 5 \times 2$

.... **1 mark**

.... **1 mark**

g) $(2 + 5 + 3 + 7) \times (1 + 3)$

h) $8 + (2 \div 2) - 3$

.... **1 mark**

.... **1 mark**

i) $(7 + 18) \times 4$

j) $9 \div 3 - 1 + 8$

.... **1 mark**

.... **1 mark**

k) $10 + 15 - (2 \times 6)$

l) $14 + 6 \div 3 - 2$

.... **1 mark**

.... **1 mark**

2. Add brackets to these statements to make them true.

a) $20 \div 2 + 8 = 2$

b) $10 + 15 \div 2 + 3 = 5$

2 marks

Fractions

1. What fraction of each pizza is left?

a)

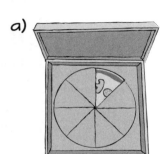

....   1 mark

b)

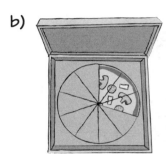

....   1 mark

2. Look at these shapes. For each shape, write down the approximate fraction that is unshaded.

a)

....   1 mark

b)

....   1 mark

3. Shade the given fraction of each of these shapes.

a) $\dfrac{3}{5}$

First count how many parts of the diagram make $\dfrac{1}{5}$

1 mark

b) $\dfrac{3}{8}$

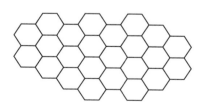

1 mark

Equivalent fractions

1. Fill in the gaps in these pairs of equivalent fractions.

Look for common factors.

a) $\dfrac{4}{12} = \dfrac{\square}{3}$

1 mark

b) $\dfrac{3}{5} = \dfrac{9}{\square}$

1 mark

c) $\dfrac{5}{\square} = \dfrac{30}{48}$

1 mark

d) $\dfrac{\square}{40} = \dfrac{7}{8}$

1 mark

2. Write down all of the fractions from this list that are equivalent to one another.

$\dfrac{3}{4}$ $\dfrac{2}{5}$ $\dfrac{3}{8}$ $\dfrac{9}{12}$ $\dfrac{12}{16}$ $\dfrac{6}{10}$

.... 2 marks

3. Boyd says that the fraction $\dfrac{111}{207}$ is in its simplest form. Is he correct? Explain your answer.

....

....

.... 1 mark

Comparing fractions

1. For each pair of fractions, write the correct symbol (<, > or =) to make the statements true.

> Look for common multiples of the denominators.

a) $\dfrac{4}{5}$ .... > .... $\dfrac{2}{3}$ 1 mark   b) $\dfrac{7}{10}$ .... $\dfrac{3}{4}$ 1 mark

c) $\dfrac{5}{8}$ .... $\dfrac{30}{48}$ 1 mark   d) $\dfrac{5}{7}$ .... $\dfrac{3}{8}$ 1 mark

2. Each diagram below is divided into equal sections. Shade $\dfrac{3}{5}$ of each diagram.

a)   b) 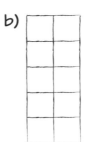   c)

        1 mark   1 mark   1 mark

3. Alicia and James both receive the same amount of pocket money. James spent $\dfrac{2}{5}$ of his pocket money on sweets. Alicia spent $\dfrac{5}{8}$ of her pocket money on sweets. Alicia said she had spent more money on sweets than James. Is Alicia correct? Explain your answer.

....

.... 2 marks

Adding and subtracting fractions

1. Add these fractions.

> To add fractions with different denominators, first change them to equivalent fractions with the same denominator.

a) $\dfrac{3}{4} + \dfrac{1}{8}$

$\dfrac{3}{4} = \dfrac{6}{8}$

$\dfrac{6}{8} + \dfrac{1}{8} = \dfrac{7}{8}$

..........$\dfrac{7}{8}$.......... 1 mark

b) $\dfrac{2}{5} + \dfrac{1}{10}$

.... 1 mark

c) $\dfrac{2}{3} + \dfrac{1}{12}$

.... 1 mark

d) $\dfrac{1}{6} + \dfrac{5}{18}$

.... 1 mark

2. Subtract these fractions.

a) $\dfrac{4}{5} - \dfrac{3}{10}$

.... 1 mark

b) $\dfrac{11}{12} - \dfrac{3}{4}$

.... 1 mark

3. In a class of children, $\dfrac{3}{4}$ of the children have brown eyes, one fifth have blue eyes and the rest have green eyes. What fraction of the class has green eyes?

.... 3 marks

Multiplying fractions

1. Multiply these fractions. Give your answers in their simplest form.

a) $\dfrac{3}{4} \times \dfrac{1}{2}$

$\dfrac{3 \times 1}{4 \times 2} = \dfrac{3}{8}$

$\dfrac{3}{8}$

.... 1 mark

b) $\dfrac{3}{5} \times \dfrac{3}{8}$

> Do any cancelling first, before multiplying numerators together and then denominators together.

.... 1 mark

c) $\dfrac{2}{3} \times \dfrac{1}{4}$

.... 1 mark

d) $\dfrac{3}{10} \times \dfrac{5}{9}$

.... 1 mark

2. Put numbers into these boxes to make a correct multiplication.

a) $\dfrac{2}{\square} \times \dfrac{\square}{10} = \dfrac{2}{5}$

.... 2 marks

b) $\dfrac{3}{\square} \times \dfrac{\square}{4} = \dfrac{5}{8}$

.... 2 marks

3. Padmini ate one quarter of a cake. Her brother ate half of what was left. Padmini says, 'There's only $\dfrac{3}{8}$ of the cake left now'. Is she correct? Explain how you know.

....

.... 2 marks

24

Dividing fractions

1. Divide these fractions.

a) $\frac{3}{4} \div 5$

$\frac{3}{4 \times 5} = \frac{3}{20}$

$\frac{3}{20}$

.... 1 mark

b) $\frac{4}{5} \div 3$

> To divide any fraction by a whole number, multiply the denominator by that number to find a new denominator. Then simplify if you can.

.... 1 mark

c) $\frac{2}{3} \div 4$

.... 1 mark

d) $\frac{8}{9} \div 6$

.... 1 mark

2. Put numbers into these boxes to make a correct division.

a) $\frac{4}{\square} \div 3 = \frac{4}{39}$

1 mark

b) $\frac{\square}{10} \div 2 = \frac{3}{20}$

1 mark

3. Frank bought a cheesecake for himself and his three children. He gave himself a third of the cheesecake and shared the rest out between his children. What fraction of the cheesecake did each child get?

.... 2 marks

4. Andrew was told to divide one half by three. Sophia was told to divide one third by two. Their dad said they would get the same answer. Was their dad correct? Explain your answer.

....

.... 2 marks

Fractions and decimals

1. Fill in the gaps in this table to convert between these fractions and decimals.

fraction		$\frac{1}{8}$			$\frac{2}{5}$	$\frac{1}{2}$		$\frac{3}{4}$
decimal	0.1		0.2	0.25			0.6	

8 marks

2. Write down a fraction and a decimal to show how much of each shape has been shaded.

a)

b)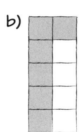

c)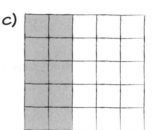

....   3 marks

3. Change these decimals to fractions.

a) 0.2 =

....   1 mark

b) 0.25 =

....   1 mark

c) 0.3 =

....   1 mark

d) 0.375 =

....   1 mark

4. Change these fractions into decimals.

> First, cancel each fraction down as much as you can.

a) $\frac{15}{20}$

....   1 mark

b) $\frac{8}{20}$

....   1 mark

c) $\frac{9}{15}$

....   1 mark

d) $\frac{10}{25}$

....   1 mark

Multiplying decimals

1. Complete these multiplications.

   a) 7.5×5

   $7.5 \times 10 = 75$

   ```
       7 5
   ×     5
     3 7 5
       2
   ```

   $375 \div 10 = 37.5$

   ....37.5............   2 marks

   b) 21.6×4

   ....   2 marks

2. What is the cost of five packs of stamps if each pack costs £1.35?

   ....   2 marks

3. Dan is making apple chutney to sell at a fair.

   Apples cost £1.40 per kg.

   Sugar costs 78p per kg.

   5 glass jars cost £4.35 altogether.

   > Think carefully about what you need to multiply together to find each cost.

   Dan uses 15 kg of apples and 11 kg of sugar to make 25 full jars of chutney. Find the total cost to make the 25 jars of chutney.

   ....   3 marks

Percentages

1. There were 100 pupils in a school. 40 of the pupils were boys.
   35 of the pupils brought a packed lunch to school.

   a) What percentage of pupils were:

      i) boys?   .... 40% .... 1 mark

      ii) girls?   .... 1 mark

   b) What percentage of pupils:

      i) brought a packed lunch to school?   .... 1 mark

      ii) didn't bring a packed lunch to school? .... 1 mark

2. Shade 50% of each of these shapes.

   a)   b)   What fraction is the same
                                                     amount as 50%?

                1 mark   1 mark

3. In a school, the pupils were asked to choose their favourite animal.
   10% of the pupils chose dogs. 60% chose cats. What percentage of
   pupils chose something else?

                                         .... 2 marks

4. Billy was told that 55% of the pupils in a school were boys. He said,
   'That means there are more boys in the school than girls.' Is Billy correct?
   Explain your answer.

   ....

   .... 3 marks

Converting percentages

1. Complete the boxes to match these decimals, fractions and percentages.

a)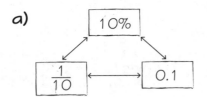

b)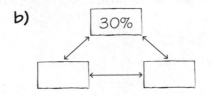

c)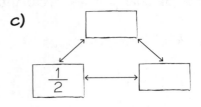

1 mark   1 mark   1 mark

2. Write down what percentage of each shape has been shaded.

> Find the fraction, then change that to a percentage.

a)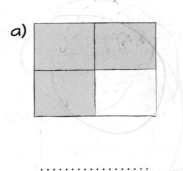

b)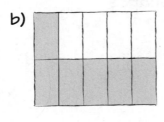

c)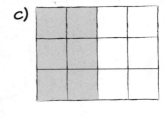

....   3 marks

3. In a school, 40% of the children go to an after school club.

a) What percentage don't go to a club?

....   1 mark

b) There are 200 pupils at this school. How many go to a club?

....   1 mark

Percentages of amounts

1. Work out these percentages.

   a) 10% of £70

   £70 ÷ 10 = £7

   .... £7 .... 1 mark

   b) 50% of 80 kg

   .... 1 mark

2. Work out these percentages.

   a) 10% of £90

   .... 1 mark

   b) 5% of £90

   > Halve 10% to find 5%.

   .... 1 mark

   c) 15% of £90

   .... 1 mark

   d) 55% of £90

   .... 1 mark

3. What is:

   a) 25% of £4?

   .... 1 mark

   b) 25% of 40 kg?

   .... 1 mark

   c) 75% of £4?

   .... 1 mark

   d) 75% of 40 kg?

   .... 1 mark

4. In Chloe's school there are 300 pupils. Chloe is told that 55% of the pupils are boys.

   She says, 'There must be 135 boys.' Is Chloe correct? Explain your answer.

   ....

   .... 2 marks

Ratio

1. Write the ratio of white squares to shaded squares for each diagram.

   a) ....5:3........ 1 mark

   b) ....4.3........ 1 mark

   c) .... 1 mark

2. Write the ratio of shaded squares to white squares for each diagram in its simplest form.

   > Divide both sides of the ratio by any common factors to simplify.

   a) .... 1 mark

   b) .... 1 mark

   c) .... 1 mark

3. Orange soda is made using 250 ml of orange with 600 ml of soda. What is the ratio of orange to soda? Write your answer in its simplest form.

   .... 1 mark

4. Terry has a bag of jelly babies. Six are red and four are yellow.
   He says that the ratio of red jelly babies to yellow jelly babies is 3 : 2
   Is he correct? Explain how you know.

   ....

   .... 2 marks

Sharing with ratio

1. Divide these amounts in the given ratios.

a) £800 in the ratio of 5 : 3

   5 + 3 = 8

   £800 ÷ 8 = £100

   5 × £100 = £500

   3 × £100 = £300

   £500 : £300
   ....   2 marks

b) 560 kg in the ratio 2 : 5

   ....   2 marks

c) 250 g in the ratio 7 : 3

   ....   2 marks

d) 369 m in the ratio 1 : 2

   ....   2 marks

2. In a pie eating competition, James and Bessie ate 45 pies in the ratio of 5 : 4
   How many pies did they each eat?

   James: ....

   Bessie: ....

   3 marks

3. A drink of spicy ginger was made by mixing ginger ale
   and peppermint essence in the ratio of 9 : 1   1 litre = 1,000 ml
   How much of each is needed to make 1 litre of the drink?

   ginger ale: ....

   peppermint essence: ....

   3 marks

Proportion

1. There are 30 jelly babies in a box.
   8 are red, 12 are yellow and the rest
   are green.

   Give your answers as fractions in their simplest form.

   What proportion are:

   a) red jelly babies?   **b)** green jelly babies?

   $$\frac{8}{30} = \frac{4}{15}$$

   $$\frac{4}{15}$$
   .... 1 mark   .... 1 mark

2. Abdul makes some jam. He uses 3 cups of strawberries to 1 cup of sugar.
   What proportion of the jam is:

   a) strawberries? .... 1 mark

   b) sugar? .... 1 mark

3. Three cows on a farm produce a total of 90 litres of milk per day.
   Daisy produces 40 litres, Buttercup produces 25 litres and Rosie
   produces the rest. What proportion of the milk does each cow produce?

   Daisy: ....   Buttercup: ....   Rosie: ....

4. In a box of chocolates, 12 have hard centres and 8 have soft centres.

   Kerri says that $\frac{2}{3}$ of the chocolates have hard centres. Is Kerri correct?
   Explain your answer.

   ....

   .... 2 marks

Scale factors

1. This shape has been enlarged by a scale factor of 3

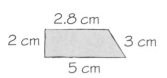

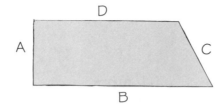

What are the new measurements of the sides A, B, C and D?

A = ...

B = ...

C = ...

D = ...   **4 marks**

2. In this triangle, A is 3 cm, B is 4 cm and C is 5 cm. Complete the table to show the lengths of the sides after different enlargements.

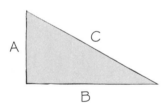

scale factor	A	B	C
2	6 cm		
4			
7			

8 marks

3. A square has sides of length 7 cm. It is enlarged so that its perimeter is 140 cm. What scale factor was used to enlarge the square?

> The perimeter of a square is four times the length of each side.

....   **3 marks**

Using letters

1. If $m = 13$, find the value of:

   a) $m + 7$

   b) $2m - 3$

   .... 1 mark   .... 1 mark

2. Find the value of the letter in each number sentence.

   a) $m + 7 = 15$

   b) $d \times 5 = 15$

   $m =$ .... 1 mark $d =$ .... 1 mark

   c) $4k - 5 = 15$

   $k =$ .... 1 mark

3. In brick wall puzzles, the sum of any two bricks that are side-by-side is shown on the brick directly above them. For these puzzles, find n.

   a)
   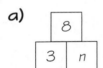

   b)
   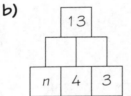

   c)
   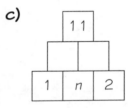

   $3 + n = 8$

   $n = 8 - 3$

   $n =$ ....5.... 1 mark $n =$ .... 1 mark $n =$ .... 1 mark

4. Mandy thinks of a number. She adds 5 and then multiplies by 2 to get the answer 24. What number was Mandy thinking of?

   > Work backwards from 24 using inverse operations.

   .... 2 marks

Simple formulas

1. The area of a triangle is found by using the formula: area = $\frac{1}{2}$ (base × height)

   What are the areas of the triangles with these measurements?

   a) base of 3 cm and height of 12 cm

   ....   **2 marks**

   b) both base and height of 5 cm

   ....   **2 marks**

2. A window cleaner has a formula for calculating how much to charge:

   charge = number of windows × £2 + £5

   a) How much will she charge Mrs Roberts who has 4 windows cleaned?

   ....   **2 marks**

   b) How much will she charge Mr Charlton who has 9 windows cleaned?

   ....   **2 marks**

   c) The window cleaner charges Mr Rafiq £17. She told Mr Rafiq she had cleaned 8 windows for him. Did she charge Mr Rafiq the correct amount? Explain your answer.

   ....

   ....   **2 marks**

Two unknowns

1. The shapes represent numbers. Look at the calculations and think of numbers the shapes could stand for.

   Write your answers in the tables. Write two answers for each part.

   a)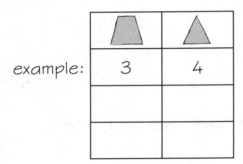

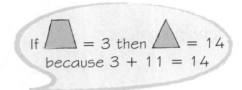

⬟	▲
example: 3	4

   2 marks

   b) ⬟ − ▲ = 8

⬟	▲
example: 10	2

   2 marks

2. Jenny and Michael have £6.50 pocket money between them. Neither of them has more than £4.00 or less than 50p. List three possible amounts that they could each have.

Jenny			
Michael			

   3 marks

Linear sequences

1. Complete these sequences.

> Use the difference between the 1st and the 3rd terms to find the term-to-term rule.

a) 3,   7, ...11......,   15, ...19......, ...23....   2 marks

b) 2, ...,   8, ...,   14, ...   2 marks

2. Complete this sequence and find the term-to-term rule.

1, ...,   19, ...,   37, ...   3 marks

term-to-term rule: ....

....   5 marks

3. A rule that can be used to generate a sequence is 'add 5 to the previous term'.

a) The second term of a sequence using this rule is 12
Write down the next four terms.

.... , ... , ... , ...   2 marks

b) The third term of a different sequence using this rule is 21
Write down the first six terms.

.... , ... , ... , ... , ... , ...   2 marks

4. The second term of a linear sequence is 16. The fifth term is 37. Saiqa said, 'The third term must be 23.' Is Saiqa correct? Explain your answer.

....

....   2 marks

Answers

NUMBER

1 Place value

1. 12,184

2. three hundred and twenty-four thousand, six hundred and seventy-two

3. 299, 456, 472, 575, 901

4. a) 56 > 50   b) 76 < 77

5. B

6. 32 × 4 (= 128)

2 Negative numbers

1. a) 5 degrees   b) −3°C

2. −1 and 1

3. a) 10 degrees   b) −4°C

3 Decimal numbers

1. 0.75, 0.7, 0.8 and 0.66

2. 6.7

3. 0.11, 1.001, 1.01, 1.101

4. Any three decimals greater than 0 that add to make a total of 0.1 (e.g. 0.02, 0.03 and 0.05)

4 Rounding

1. a) 627 rounds to 600, 474 rounds to 500, 412 rounds to 400

   b) 531 rounds to 500, 617 rounds to 600, 253 rounds to 300, 474 rounds to 500

2. a) 500   b) 240   c) 3,000

3. 1,070 rounds to 1,000, 8,225 rounds to 8,000, 3,680 rounds to 4,000

5 Rounding decimals

1. a) 8.2   b) 0.4   c) 100.2   d) 0.0

2. a) 1.25   b) 23.52   c) 43.33   d) 0.12

3. 16 seconds

4. 38p

6 Roman numerals

1. a) 8   b) 95   c) 39   d) 540

2. 500 + 100 − 50 = 550

3. 1992

4. b) day of the month: XXIII   month: I   year: MCMXCIII

CALCULATION

7 Written addition

1. a) 973   b) 818   c) 2.07   d) 10,498

2.

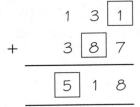

3. 6,829

8 Written subtraction

1. a) 560   b) 2.4   c) 217   d) 11,697

2. 427

3. 2,981 km

4.
```
   ³4̶ ¹5 [6]
 -   2 [7] 4
   ─────────
     [1] 8 2
```

9 Estimating
1. 250g
2. answers between 60 and 75
3. 19,000 or 20,000
4. 45,000 or 50,000

10 Multiples
1. a) 18, 42, 422, 16
   b) 3, 63, 18, 42, 9
2. a) 84   b) 97
3.

	less than 100	100 or more
multiples of 20	80	640
not multiples of 20	22	102

11 Factors
1. 60, 90
2. 1, 2, 5, 10
3. factors of 30: 6   factors of 40: 8
   common factors
   of 30 and 40: 5   outside the diagram: 7
4. 1 by 81, 3 by 27 or 9 by 9

12 Prime numbers
1. 29 and 59
2. 23
3. She is incorrect. 7 and 11 are factors of 77
4. prime and odd: 17   not prime and even: 20   not prime and odd: 9

13 Square numbers
1. a) 16   b) 100   c) 25   d) 2,500
2.

	even	not even
square numbers	16	25, 1
not square numbers	14, 8	11

3. 9 and 36
4. 5

14 Cube numbers
1. a) 216   b) 1   c) 64   d) 1,000
2. $7^3 = 343$ $5^3 = 125$ $3^3 = 27$ $10^3 = 1,000$ $1^3 = 1$
3. $8 \times 8 = 64$ and $4 \times 4 \times 4 = 64$
4. 27

15 Short multiplication
1 a) 144   b) 66   c) 1,012   d) 2,360
2 525 cm or 5.25 m
3 156

40

Answers

16 Long multiplication
1. a) 384   b) 352   c) 682   d) 1,288
2. £442
3. 576

17 Short division
1. a) 14   b) 24   c) 121   d) 21
2. 5
3. 32 and 27
4. 75

18 Long division
1. a) 28 r 12   b) 42   c) 34 r 14   d) 33 r 19
2. 18

19 Order of operations
1. a) 15   b) 10   c) 71   d) 2
   e) 21   f) 2   g) 68   h) 6
   i) 100   j) 10   k) 13   l) 14
2. a) $20 \div (2 + 8) = 2$
   b) $(10 + 15) \div (2 + 3) = 5$

FRACTIONS, DECIMALS AND PERCENTAGES

20 Fractions

1. a) $\frac{1}{8}$ b) $\frac{3}{10}$

2. a) $\frac{1}{4}$ b) $\frac{2}{3}$

3. a) any six cells shaded   b) any nine cells shaded

21 Equivalent fractions
1. a) 1   b) 15   c) 8   d) 35

2. $\frac{3}{4}, \frac{9}{12}, \frac{12}{16}$

3. No, both the numerator and denominator can be divided by 3 to get $\frac{37}{69}$.

22 Comparing fractions
1. a) >   b) <   c) =   d) >
2. a) any three cells shaded   b) any six cells shaded   c) any 12 cells shaded

3. Yes. $\frac{5}{8} = \frac{25}{40}$ and $\frac{2}{5} = \frac{16}{40}$ so $\frac{5}{8}$ is more.

23 Adding and subtracting fractions

1. a) $\frac{7}{8}$ b) $\frac{5}{10}$ or $\frac{1}{2}$

   c) $\frac{9}{12}$ or $\frac{3}{4}$ d) $\frac{8}{18}$ or $\frac{4}{9}$

2. a) $\frac{5}{10}$ or $\frac{1}{2}$ b) $\frac{2}{12}$ or $\frac{1}{6}$

3. $\frac{1}{20}$

24 Multiplying fractions

1. a) $\frac{3}{8}$ b) $\frac{9}{40}$ c) $\frac{1}{6}$ d) $\frac{1}{6}$

2. a) There is more than one correct answer, for example: $\frac{2}{3} \times \frac{6}{10}$

   b) There is more than one correct answer, for example: $\frac{3}{6} \times \frac{5}{4}$

3. Yes. $1 - \frac{1}{4} = \frac{3}{4}$; $\frac{3}{4} \times \frac{1}{2} = \frac{3}{8}$

25 Dividing fractions

1. a) $\frac{3}{20}$ b) $\frac{4}{15}$

   c) $\frac{2}{12}$ or $\frac{1}{6}$ d) $\frac{8}{54}$ or $\frac{4}{27}$

2. a) 13   b) 3

3. $\frac{2}{9}$

4. Yes, the answer to both is $\frac{1}{6}$.

26 Fractions and decimals

1.

fraction	$\frac{1}{10}$	$\frac{1}{8}$	$\frac{1}{5}$	$\frac{1}{4}$	$\frac{2}{5}$	$\frac{1}{2}$	$\frac{3}{5}$	$\frac{3}{4}$
decimal	0.1	0.125	0.2	0.25	0.4	0.5	0.6	0.75

2. a) $\frac{3}{4}$, 0.75   b) $\frac{3}{5}$, 0.6   c) $\frac{2}{5}$, 0.4

3. a) $\frac{1}{5}$ b) $\frac{1}{4}$ c) $\frac{3}{10}$ d) $\frac{3}{8}$

4. a) 0.75   b) 0.4   c) 0.6   d) 0.4

27 Multiplying decimals

1. a) 37.5   b) 86.4

2. £6.75

3. £51.33

28 Percentages

1. a) i) 40%   ii) 60%   b) i) 35%   ii) 65%

2. a) half shaded   b) half shaded

3. 30%

4. Yes, because 55% is more than half OR because 55% is more than 45%.

29 Converting percentages

1. a) $\frac{1}{10}$, 0.1   b) $\frac{3}{10}$, 0.3   c) 50%, 0.5

2. a) 75%   b) 60%   c) 50%

3. a) 60%   b) 80

30 Percentages of amounts

1. a) £7   b) 40 kg

2. a) £9   b) £4.50

   c) £13.50   d) £49.50

3. a) £1   b) 10 kg   c) £3   d) 30 kg

4. No, because 55% of 300 is 165. You can easily see that it can't be 135 because 50% of 300 is 150, so there must be more than 150 boys.

Answers

RATIO

31 Ratio
1. a) $5:3$ b) $4:3$ c) $6:2$ or $3:1$
2. a) $1:2$ b) $3:1$ c) $1:3$
3. $5:12$
4. Yes, he is correct. You can simplify $6:4$ to $3:2$

32 Sharing with ratio
1. a) £500:£300   b) 160kg:400kg   c) 175g:75g   d) 123m:246m
2. James: 25 pies, Bessie: 20 pies
3. Ginger ale: 900ml, peppermint essence: 100ml

33 Proportion
1. a) $\frac{4}{15}$ b) $\frac{1}{3}$
2. a) $\frac{3}{4}$ b) $\frac{1}{4}$
3. Daisy: $\frac{40}{90}$ or $\frac{4}{9}$, Buttercup: $\frac{25}{90}$ or $\frac{5}{18}$, Rosie: $\frac{25}{90}$ or $\frac{5}{18}$
4. No, the fraction is $\frac{12}{20}$ which cancels to $\frac{3}{5}$

34 Scale factors
1. A = 6cm, B = 15cm, C = 9cm, D = 8.4cm
2.

scale factor	A	B	C
2	6cm	8cm	10cm
4	12cm	16cm	20cm
7	21cm	28cm	35cm

3. 5

ALGEBRA

35 Using letters
1. a) 20   b) 23
2. a) $m = 8$ b) $d = 3$ c) $k = 5$
3. a) $n = 5$ b) $n = 2$ c) $n = 4$
4. 7

36 Simple formulas
1. a) $18\,cm^2$ b) $12.5\,cm^2$
2. a) £13   b) £23   c) No, she should have charged him £21

37 Two unknowns
1. a) answers include: 4 and 15, 5 and 16   b) answers include: 11 and 3, 12 and 4
2. answers include:

Jenny	£3.50	£2.50	£3.25
Michael	£3.00	£4.00	£3.25

38 Linear sequences
1. a) 11, 19, 23   b) 5, 11, 17
2. 10, 28, 46   add 9 to the previous term
3. a) 17, 22, 27, 32   b) 11, 16, 21, 26, 31, 36
4. Yes, the term-to-term rule is add 7, 16 + 7 = 23

Published by Pearson Education Limited, 80 Strand, London, WC2R 0RL.

www.pearsonschools.co.uk

Text © Pearson Education Limited 2016
Edited by Elektra Media Ltd
Typeset by Elektra Media Ltd
Produced by Elektra Media Ltd
Original illustrations © Pearson Education Limited 2016
Illustrated by Elektra Media Ltd
Cover illustration by Ana Albero

The rights of Christopher Bishop and Brian Speed to be identified as authors of this work have been asserted by them in accordance with the Copyright, Designs and Patents Act 1988.

First published 2016

19 18 17 16
10 9 8 7 6 5 4 3 2 1

British Library Cataloguing in Publication Data
A catalogue record for this book is available from the British Library.

ISBN 978 1 292 14623 2

Printed in Italy by L.E.G.O. S.p.A.